CW00406437

clarinet duets

for two clarinets

für zwei Klarinetten

james rae

www.universaledition.com

vienna · london · new york

UE 16552

ISMN 979-0-008-04280-5
UPC 8-03452-04080-4
ISBN 978-3-7024-3027-6

EASY JAZZY SERIES

The JAZZY SERIES was written to provide players of moderate abilities with experience of the syncopated patterns of jazz.

Now, the EASY JAZZIES offer this opportunity to players at an earlier stage of their musical development and provide a perfect stepping-stone to the abundance of solo and duet material in the main series.

JAZZY SERIES soll auch nicht so weit fortgeschrittenen Musikern die Gelegenheit geben, sich mit den synkopierten Rhythmen des Jazz vertraut zu machen.

Mit der Serie EASY JAZZIES bietet sich diese Gelegenheit jungen Musikern nun bereits zu einem früheren Zeitpunkt ihrer musikalischen Entwicklung. Die Stücke stellen ein ideales „Sprungbrett" für das reichhaltige Solo- und Duomaterial der Hauptserie dar.

EASY JAZZY DUETS – CLARINETS *BY* JAMES RAE

This collection of ten easy jazzy duets has been written entirely in the low register to enable players of very modest abilities to tackle them without difficulty. For ease of reading, the parts have been printed on separate pages. Chord symbols at concert pitch have been included in the second part for keyboard or guitar accompaniment.

N.B. In most of the pieces the quavers are to be played in 'swing time':

i.e. ♫ = ♩♪   and ♫♫ = ♩♪♩♪

Die vorliegende Sammlung besteht aus zehn leichten Jazzduos, die ausschließlich im tiefen Register geschrieben sind, so dass sie auch von Klarinettisten mit sehr bescheidenen technischen Fertigkeiten problemlos bewältigt werden können. Um der besseren Lesbarkeit willen wurden die beiden Stimmen auf getrennten Seiten gedruckt. Zur Begleitung mit Keyboard oder Gitarre sind in der zweiten Stimme Akkordsymbole angegeben.

P.S.: In den meisten dieser Stücke sind die Achtelnoten im „Swing-Rhythmus" zu spielen,

z.B. ♫ = ♩♪   und ♫♫ = ♩♪♩♪

CONTENTS

Part 1

BLUE ROCK

James Rae

Heavy!

BLUE ROCK

Part 2

James Rae

* Chord symbols at concert pitch.

Part 1

SUNDAY AFTERNOON

James Rae

Steady swing feel

Part 2

❷

SUNDAY AFTERNOON

James Rae

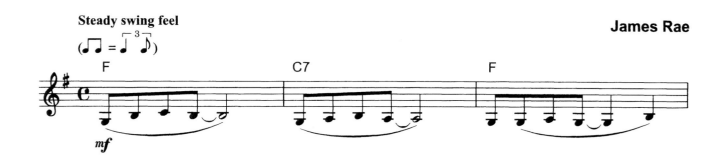

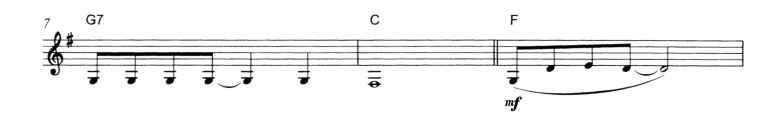

Part 1

CHASIN' THE BLUES

James Rae

Fast swing tempo

CHASIN' THE BLUES

Part 2

James Rae

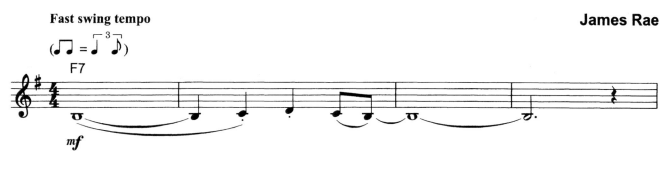

Part 1

❹

SWINGIN' WALTZ

Jazz waltz tempo

James Rae

❹ SWINGIN' WALTZ

Part 2

James Rae

Part 1

❺

THE SLIPPERY SLOPE

James Rae

THE SLIPPERY SLOPE

Part 2

James Rae

UNDER SUSPICION

James Rae

Jazz waltz tempo

Part 2

UNDER SUSPICION

Jazz waltz tempo

James Rae

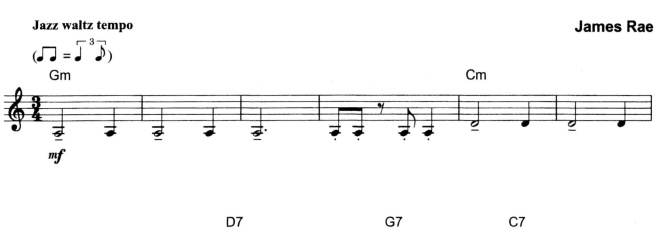

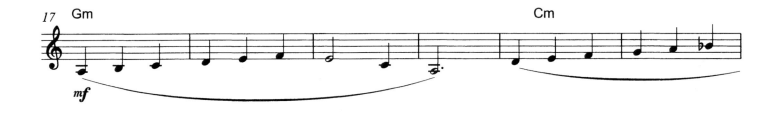

LEAPS AND BOUNDS

Part 1

James Rae

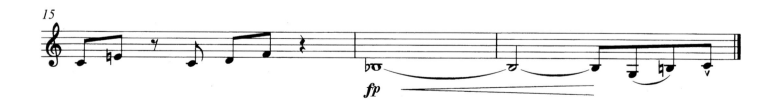

LEAPS AND BOUNDS

Part 2

James Rae

Bright swing tempo

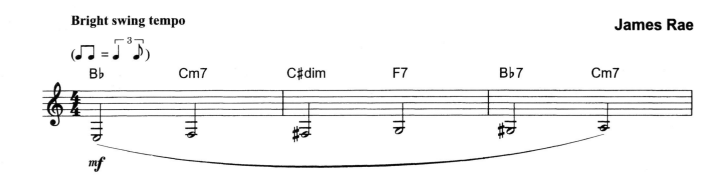

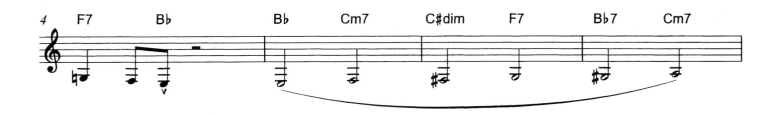

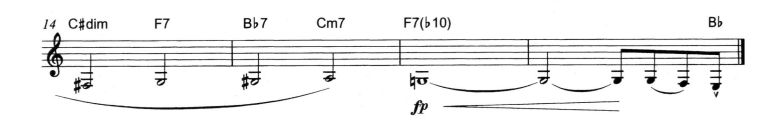

8 THE CLASH!

Part 1

James Rae

Part 2

THE CLASH!

James Rae

⑨

BENEATH THE SURFACE

Part 1

James Rae

BENEATH THE SURFACE

Part 2

James Rae

🔟

CLEARWAY

Part 1

James Rae

Part 2

CLEARWAY

James Rae

Further easy titles in lighter styles for the clarinet

■ JAZZ

Paul Harvey • Easy Jazzy Clarinet for clarinet and piano (1–3) • UE 19214

James Rae • Easy Jazzy Clarinet Duets for two clarinets (2–3) • UE 16552

James Rae • Easy Jazzy Flute & Clarinet Duets for flute & clarinet (2–3) • UE 16588

James Rae • Jazz Scale Studies for solo clarinet (2–4) • UE 21351

James Rae • Jazzy Clarinet Duets for two clarinets (3–4) • UE 19430

Tilmann Dehnhard • Easy Jazz Studies for Clarinet (3–5)* • UE 35996

■ BLUES

James Rae • Easy Blue Clarinet for clarinet and piano (1–3) • UE 21261

James Rae • Easy Blue Clarinet Duets for two clarinets (2–3) • UE21370

■ LATIN

James Rae • Latin Clarinet for clarinet and piano (1–4) • UE 17363

■ WORLD MUSIC – Play-along

Richard Graf • Ireland for clarinet and CD (opt. piano) (3) • UE 34145

Timna Brauer/Elias Meiri • Israel for clarinet and CD (opt. piano) (3) • UE 34146

Iwan Malachowskij • Russia for clarinet and CD (opt. piano) (3) • UE 34149

Jovino Santos Neto • Brazil for clarinet and CD (opt. piano) (4–6) • UE 34155

Diego Collatti • Argentina for clarinet and CD (opt. piano) (3–4) • UE 34161

Yale Strom • Klezmer for clarinet and CD (opt. piano) (2–5) • UE 34164

Hidan Mamudov • Balkan for clarinet and CD (opt. piano) (2–7) • UE 35573

* Approximate gradings
1–8 = Easy – Advanced